P9-CCM-945

Humble King
songbook

All transparency masters for "Humble King" can be found under the enhanced portion of the corresponding CD.

arranged for piano, vocal, choral and guitar chord charts
plus guitar tablature
as recorded on the Vineyard Music USA release
"Humble King" (VMD9400R)

Sku# VMB9400

piano transcription by MusicTranscription.com

ADORAMUS TE

DEAN SALYN

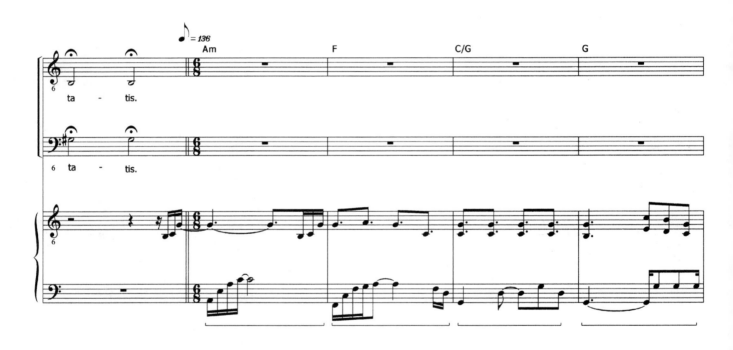

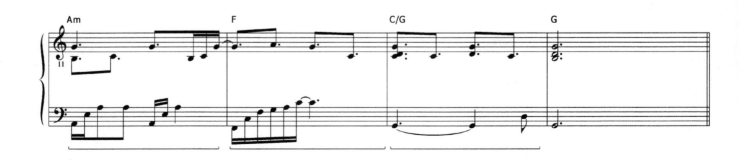

Ho - - - ly night, dawns with the Sa - vior's

Ho - - - ly night, dawns with the Sa - vior's

light Hope has come,

light Hope has come,

born is the Cho - sen One

born is the Cho - sen One

3

4

8

12

ADVENT CAROL

BRUCE BABAD

Measures 36-43: Improvised solo as played by Bruce Babad

Eb Alto Saxophone

Measures 43-54: Improvised solo as played by Bruce Babad

split tone

ADVENT CAROL

Bb Soprano Saxophone

BRUCE BABAD

Measures 36-43: Improvised solo as played by Bruce Babad

ADVENT CAROL

BRUCE BABAD

ANGELS FROM THE REALMS OF GLORY

JAMES MONTGOMERY
HENRY SMART

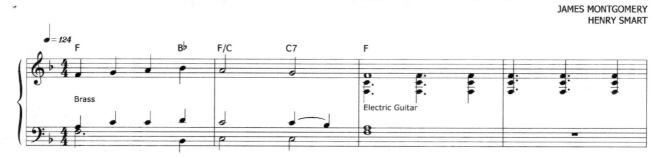

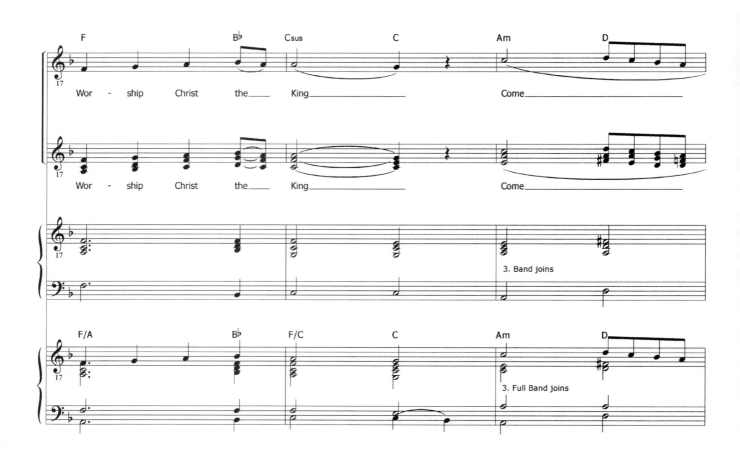

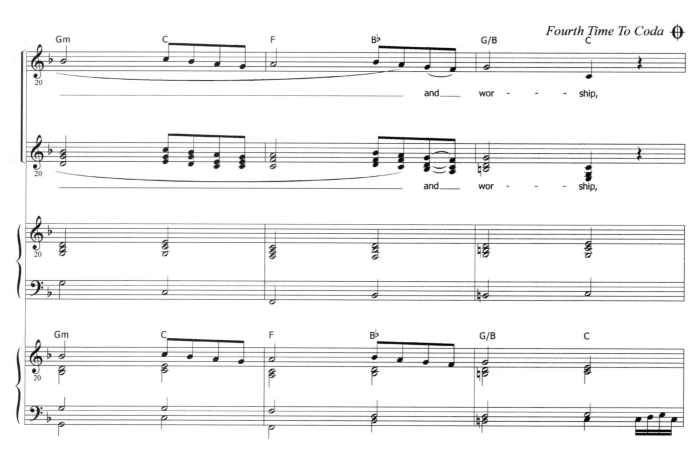

ANGELS FROM THE REALMS OF GLORY

(BRASS - Arranged, Concert Pitch)

JAMES MONTGOMERY
HENRY SMART

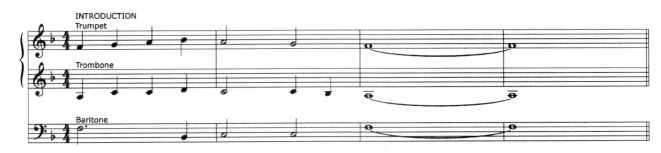

26

REPEAT CHORUS

C Trumpet Descant

29

BREATH OF HEAVEN (MARY'S SONG)

CHRIS EATON
AMY GRANT

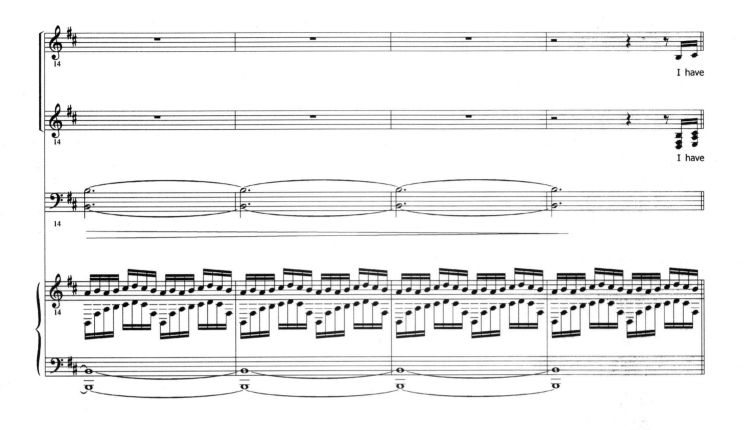

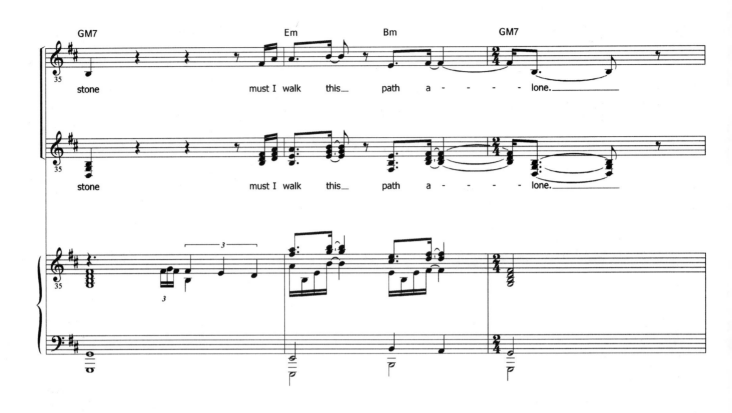

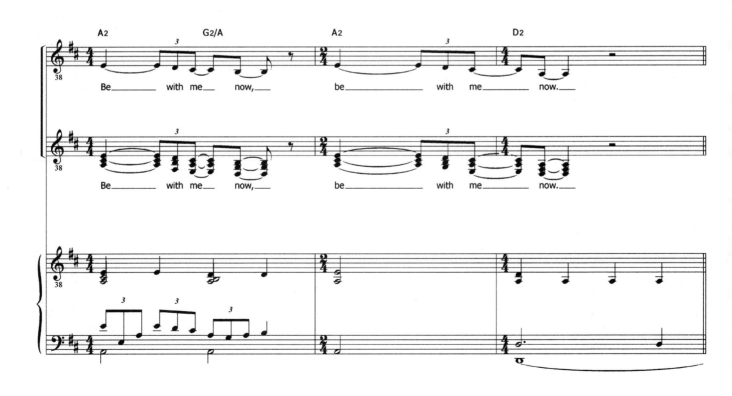

FIRST NOEL (INSTRUMENTAL)

PUBLIC DOMAIN

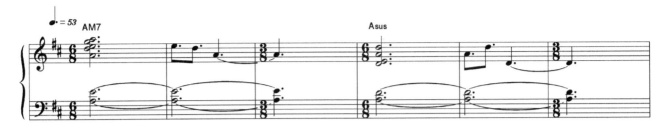

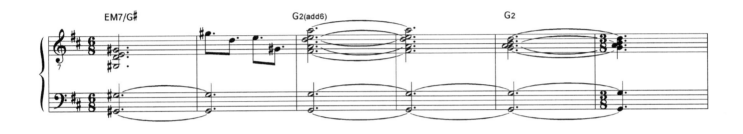

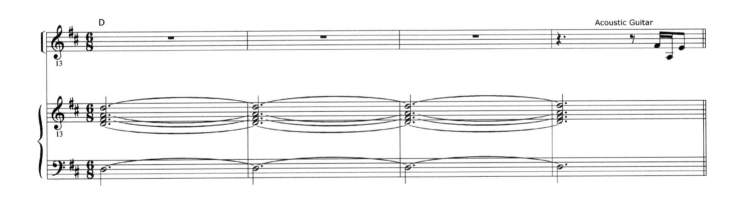

GLORY TO GOD

44

HUMBLE KING

BRENTON BROWN

Third time to Coda

50

I HEARD THE BELLS ON CHRISTMAS DAY

HENRY W. LONGFELLOW
J. BAPTISTE CALKIN

I WONDER AS I WANDER

APALACHIAN CAROL

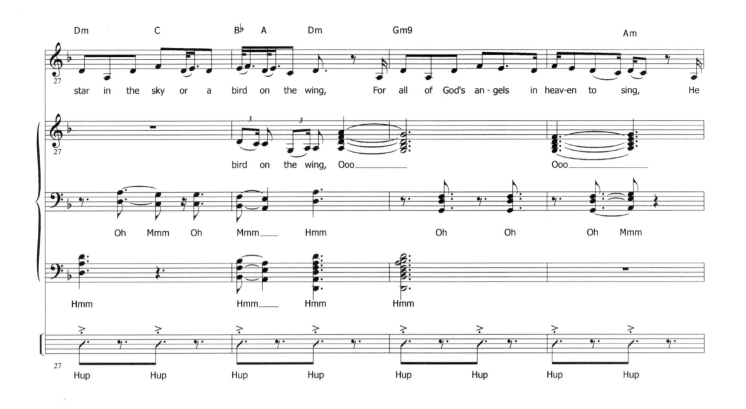

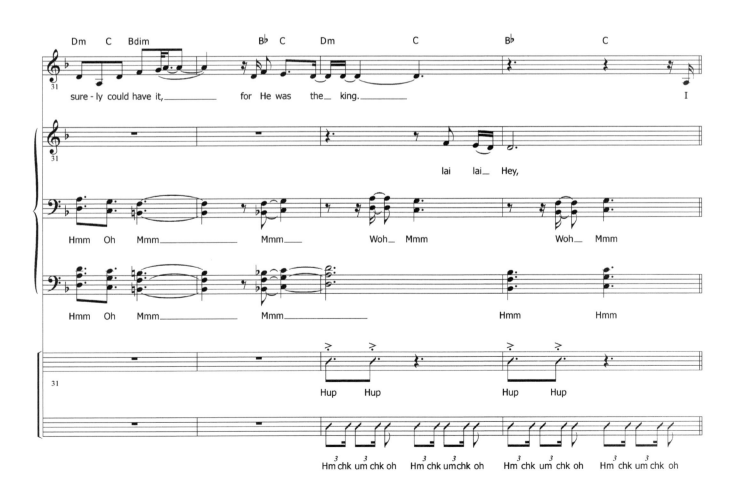

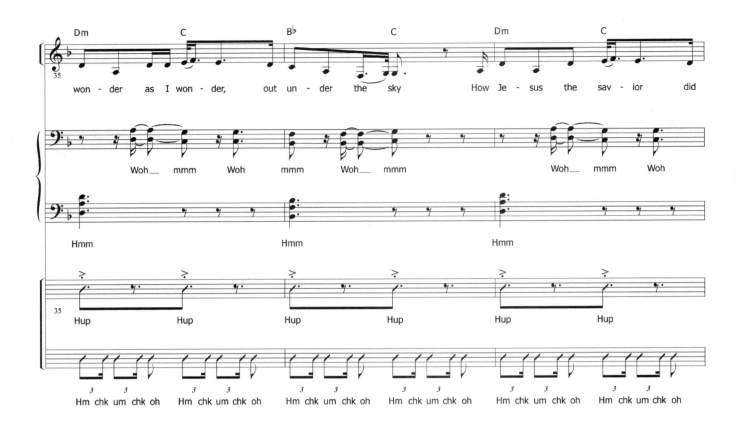

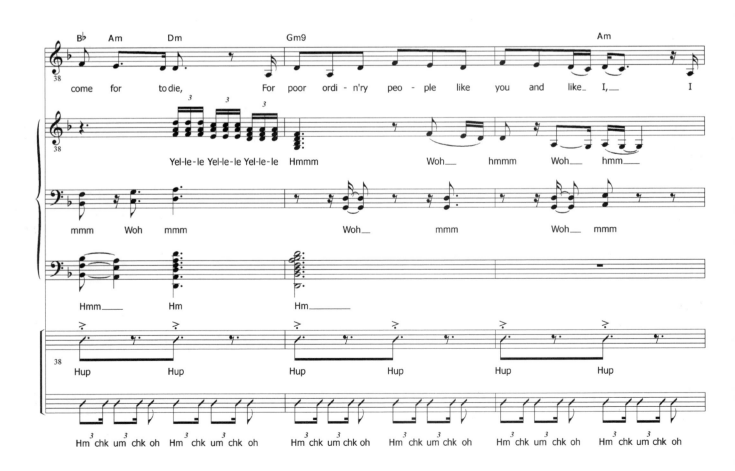

JOY TO THE WORLD

WORDS: ISSAC WATTS
MUSIC: GEORGE F. HANDEL

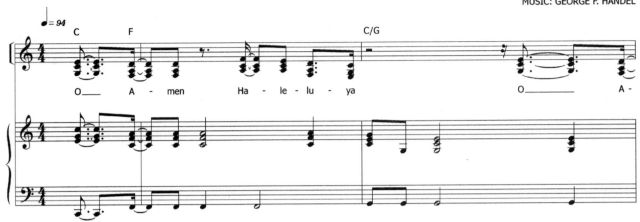

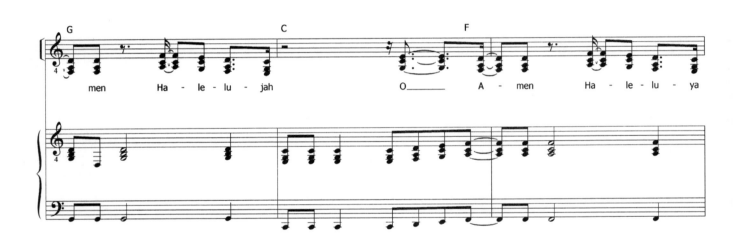

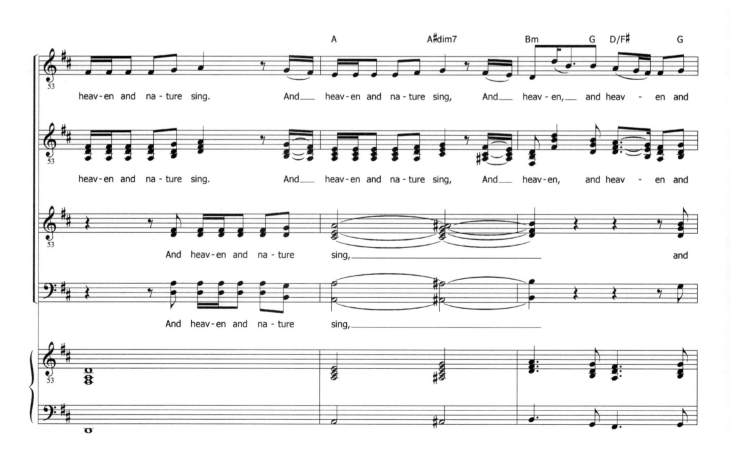

LORD COME THIS CHRISTMAS

ANDY PARK

74

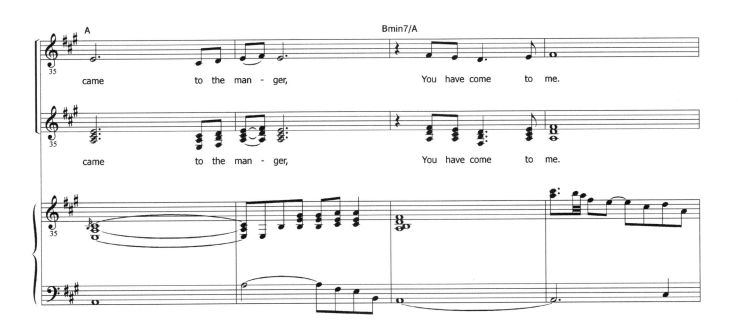

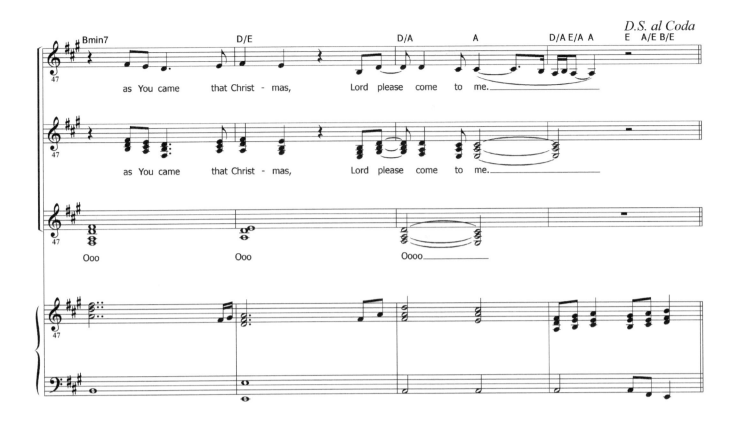

Coda

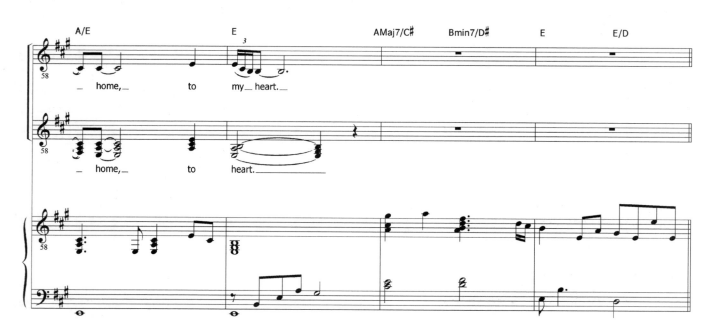

MY SOUL (MAGNIFICAT)

ADELE KANE
DAVE KANE
NICK MANDERS

84

ONCE IN ROYAL DAVID'S CITY (MEDLEY)*

CECIL FRANCES ALEXANDER
HENRY J. GAUNTLETT

God, God, God.

God, God, God.

When like stars His children crowned all in white shall wait around.

When like stars His children crowned all in white shall wait around.

SHOUT

SAROOP OOMEN

94

WEXFORD CAROL

PUBLIC DOMAIN

99

thank - ful heart and joy - ful mind the___ shep - herds went___ the babe to find. And

thank - ful heart and joy - ful mind the___ shep - herds went___ the babe to find. And

ADORAMUS TE

DEAN SALYN

Am   E Am
Gloria in excelsis Deo
Am   G   E
Et in terra pax hominibus
Am   E
Bonae voluntatis

Intro: Am F C/G G

F G Am Gsus C F   G   C
Holy night   dawns with the Savior's light
 F G Am F   G   C
Hope has come, born is the Chosen One
 F G   Am Gsus C F   G   C
Mary's heart   treasures the Word of God
 F G Am F   G   C G/B Am D/F♯
Child and King, great is the promise You bring

    Am D/F♯   G   E/G♯
Adoramus Te Adoramus Te
    Am   D/F♯ G   E/G♯
Et Laudamus Te Et Laudamus Te
    Am D/F♯   G   C/E
Adoramus Te Adoramus Te
   F   Csus/G
Iesu Christe

CCLI#3679942
©2002 Vineyard Songs (Canada). Admin. by Mercy/Vineyard Publishing (ASCAP) in the US.
All Rights Reserved. International Copyright Secured. Used By Permission.

ADORAMUS TE - continued

DEAN SALYN

F   G   Am Gsus C F   G   C

Wise men bow   before You as we do now

F G Am F   G   C

Son of Man unfold Your sovereign plan

G   A   Bm   G   A   D

You hold the stars   and You hold my heart

G   A   Bm7   G   A   D

You have been, You are, You will be, Amen

Bm E/G#   A   F#/A#

Adoramus Te Adoramus Te

Bm   E/G#   A   F#/A#

Et Laudamus Te Et Laudamus Te

Bm E/G#   A   D/F#

Adoramus Te Adoramus Te

G   G2/A Bm

Iesu Christe

GM7

Iesu Iesu Iesu Christe

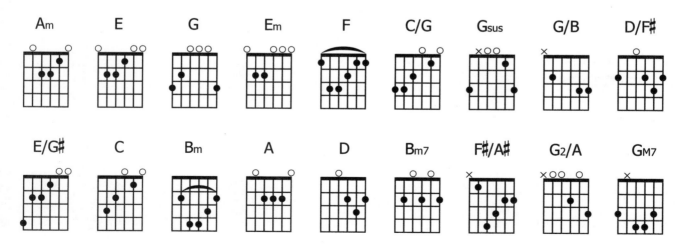

ANGELS FROM THE REALMS OF GLORY

JAMES MONTGOMERY & HENRY SMART
Arranged by Vineyard Music

F   C F F   C   F
Angels from the realms of glory, wing your flight o'er all the earth

F   C F F   C F
Ye who sang creation's story, now proclaim Messiah's birth

Am D Gm C F B♭ G/B C F   B♭ Csus C
Come...... and worship, worship Christ the King

Am D Gm C F B♭ G/B C F   B♭ Csus C F
Come...... and worship, worship Christ, the newborn King

F   C F Dm   C F
Shepherds in the fields abiding, watching o'er your flocks by night

F   C F Dm   C F
God with man is now residing; yonder shines the infant light

F   C F Dm   C F
Saints before the altar bending, watching long in hope and fear

F   C F Dm   C F
Suddenly the Lord, descending in His temple shall appear

F   C F Dm   C F
All creation, join in praising God, the Father, Spirit, Son

F   C F Dm   C F
Evermore your voices raising to the eternal three in One

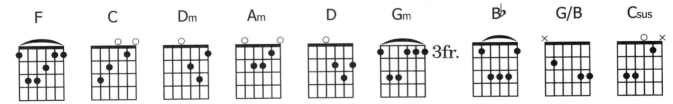

F C Dm Am D Gm B♭ G/B Csus

3fr.

CCLI#3701621
Public Domain
Arr. ©2002 Vineyard Songs (UK/Eire). Admin. by Mercy/Vineyard Publishing (ASCAP) in North America.

BREATH OF HEAVEN (Mary's Song)

CHRIS EATON AND AMY GRANT

     Bm Em/B   Bm Em/G E2
I have traveled many moonless nights
       Bm Em/B   Bm A D
Cold and weary, with a babe inside
  Em   Bm   G
And I wonder what I've done
  Em   Bm   GM7
Holy Father, You have come
  A2   G2/A   A   Bm
And chosen me now to carry Your Son

    Bm Em/B   Bm Em/G E2
I am waiting in a si-lent prayer
    Bm Em/B   Bm A D
I am frightened by the load I bear
  Em   Bm   GM7
In a world as cold as stone
     Em   Bm   GM7
Must I walk this path alone
A2   G2/A   A2   D2
Be with me now, be with me now

D   G/B   D
Breath of heaven hold me together,
Em/B F#/A# Bm   A/G   D
Be forever near me, breath of heaven
D   G/B   D
Breath of heaven, lighten my darkness,
Em/B   F#/A#   Bm
Pour over me Your holiness
A/G   D2/E   Gsus/A   Bm
For You are holy,   breath of heaven

    Bm Em/B Em/G   Bm   Em/G E2(no3rd)
Do you wonder   as You watch my face
   Bm Em/B Em/G   Bm A D
If a wi - ser   one should have had my place
  Em Bm G   Em Bm   G
But I offer all I am for the mercy of Your plan
A2   G2/A   A   G2/B A2/C# D2
Help me be strong Help me be   Help   me.

G

D/F#

Em7

C

G2

D

Em

Am/C

<u>CCLI#1128784</u>

©1992 SGO Music Publishing, Ltd. (Admin. by BUG)/Age To Age Music (Admin. by The Loving Company)
All Rights Reserved. International Copyright Secured. Used By Permission.

GLORY TO GOD

BRENTON BROWN & TERRY BUTLER

F
Glo - - ria in excelsis Deo, in excelsis De - o

      Gm7 F/A   Gm7   Csus
Peace on earth,   there is hope for everyone
      Gm7 F/A   Gm7   Csus
Tell the world,   that the saving King has come
      Eb   Bb/D   F
And His light is here for all who live in darkness
      Eb   Bb/D   Csus
And His love is here for all the broken hearted

      F/A   Bb2   Dm7   F/C C
Glory to God, glory to God, glory to God in the highest
      F/A   Bb2   Dm7   F/C C F
Glory to God, glory to God, glory to God in the high - est

Gm7   F/A   BbM7   F/A
Jesus, Messiah, the promise fulfilled, the hope of the world born for us
      Gm7   F/A   Bb   C7sus
And all who believe Him and all who receive Him are children born of God

F
Glo - - ria in excelsis Deo
F
Glo - - ria in excelsis De - o

Chord diagrams: Dm7, F/C, BbM7, C7sus, F, Bb, C, Gm7, F/A, Csus, Eb, Bb/D, Bb2

CCLI#3680326
©2002 Vineyard Songs (UK/Eire)/Mercy/Vineyard Publishing (ASCAP).
Admin. by Mercy/Vineyard Publishing in North America.
All Rights Reserved. International Copyright Secured. Used By Permission.

HUMBLE KING *[Without capo]*

BRENTON BROWN

     A♭2   E♭/G   Fm   B♭
You are the God of the broken, friend of the weak
     A♭2   E♭/G   Fm   B♭
You wash the feet of the weary, embrace the ones in need
    A♭2   E♭/G   Fm7   B♭
I want to be like You Jesus and have this heart in me
     Fm7   E♭/G   A♭2 B♭ E♭
You are the God of the humble, You are the humble King

E♭   Fm   E♭/G A♭ B♭ E♭ Fm7
 Here in this dusty ground, I bow with kings
E♭   Fm7   E♭/G A♭   B♭ E♭
 Where wise men laid before their offerings
E♭   Fm7 E♭/G A♭   B♭   Cm B♭ A♭
 I lay no golden crown here at Your feet
  E♭/G Fm7   A♭/B♭ B♭   E♭ Fm7 E♭
Just this my broken life I offer Thee

E♭   Fm   E♭/G A♭   B♭   E♭
 O kneel me down again, here at Your feet,
E♭   Fm7   E♭/G A♭2 B♭ E♭ Fm7
 Show me how much You love humility
E♭   Fm7 E♭/G A♭   B♭   Cm B♭ A♭
 Oh Spirit be the star that leads me to
  E♭/G Fm7   A♭/B♭ B♭   E♭
The humble heart of love I see in You

A♭2   E♭/G   Fm   B♭   E♭   A♭   Fm7   Cm

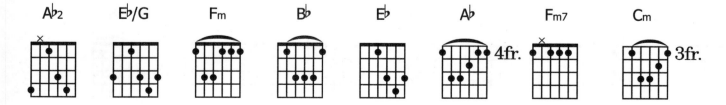

<u>CCLI#2650388</u>

©1999 Vineyard Songs (UK/Eire). Admin. by Mercy/Vineyard Publishing (ASCAP) in North America.
All Rights Reserved. International Copyright Secured. Used By Permission.

HUMBLE KING [With capo]
BRENTON BROWN

```
              G2          D/F#   Em              A
You are the God of the broken, friend of the weak
                   G2          D/F#   Em                A
You wash the feet of the weary, embrace the ones in need
              G2        D/F#   Em7              A
I want to be like You Jesus and have this heart in me
              Em7       D/F#       G2     A      D
You are the God of the humble, You are the humble King
```

```
D           Em        D/F# G   A      D    Em7
 Here in this dusty ground,  I bow with kings
D              Em7      D/F# G      A   D
 Where wise men laid before    their offerings
D        Em7   D/F#  G      A    Bm  A G
 I lay no golden crown   here at Your feet
      D/F#     Em7        G/A  A      D    Em7 D
Just this my broken life      I offer Thee
```

```
D           Em   D/F# G      A        D
 O kneel me down again,  here at Your feet,
D               Em7     D/F# G    A D Em7
 Show me how much You love  humility
D        Em7   D/F# G      A      Bm  A G
 Oh Spirit be the star  that leads me to
      D/F#     Em7       G/A  A       D
The humble heart of love   I see in You
```

Capo 1

G2   D/F#   Em   A   Em7   D   Bm   G   G/A

CCLI#2650388

I HEARD THE BELLS ON CHRISTMAS DAY

HENRY W. LONGFELLOW & J. BAPTISTE CALKIN

Arranged by Vineyard Music

D   D/F#   G/B   A$_2$/C#

I heard the bells on Christmas day

Bm   Bm/A   C#/G# C#/E#   F#m

Their old familiar car - ols   play

E$_{m7}$ A$_{9sus}$ A/G   F#m7   B$_7$

And wild and sweet   the words repeat

Em   D/F# G   G#dim A$_{7sus}$

Of peace on earth, good will to men

D   D/F#   G   A

I thought how as the day had come

Bm   Bm/A   C#/G# C#/E#   F#m7

The belfries of all Christ - en - dom

E$_{m7}$ G$_{M7}$/A   Em/G   F#dim7   B

Had rolled along   the unbroken song

Em   D/F# G   G#dim A$_{7sus}$ D A/D A G/D

Of peace on earth, good will to men

Bm   F#m7/A   Bm   A/C#

And in despair I bowed my head

G$_{M7}$ A/G   G$_{M7}$ C#/G# C#/E# F#m7

"There is no peace on earth," I   said

Em   A   F#m7   B

"For hate is strong and mocks the song

Em   D/F# G   G#dim A$_{7sus}$

Of peace on earth, good will to men"

Modulation to E: Bm7 A/B Bm Bm7 F#m7 F#(no3) E/G# F#m/A A Bsus B

CCLI#3680340

Public Domain
Arr. ©2002 Mercy/Vineyard Publishing (ASCAP).
All Rights Reserved. International Copyright Secured. Used By Permission.

I HEARD THE BELLS ON CHRISTMAS DAY - continued

HENRY W. LONGFELLOW & J. BAPTISTE CALKIN
Arranged by Vineyard Music

E   E/G#   B   A   B   E/G#
Then pealed the bells more loud and deep:

C#m   C#m/B E/B D#/A# D#/G G#m7
"God is not dead, nor does   He sleep;

F#m   A/B B/A   G#dim   C#
The wrong shall fail,   the right prevail,

F#m7 E/G# A   A G#m7 C2 C
With peace on earth,

A/C# E   D6   B(no3) B E A/E E A/E B/E E
Peace on earth, good will to men"

Simplified Chording:

Vs. 1
Line 2   Bm Bm/A   C#   F#m
    ...Their old familiar car - ols   play...

Vs. 2
Line 2   Bm Bm/A   C#   F#m7
    ...The belfries of all Christ - en - dom...

Vs. 3
Line 2   GM7   A/G GM7 C#   F#m7
    ..."There is no peace on earth," I said...

Vs. 4
Line 2   C#m   C#m/B   D#/A#   G#m7
    ..."God is not dead, nor does He sleep...

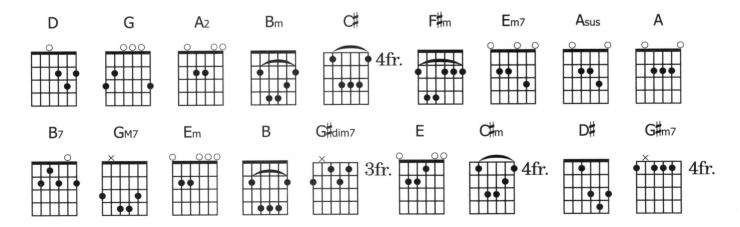

D   G   A2   Bm   C#   F#m   Em7   Asus   A

B7   GM7   Em   B   G#dim7   E   C#m   D#   G#m7

CCLI#3680340

Public Domain
Arr. ©2002 Mercy/Vineyard Publishing (ASCAP).
All Rights Reserved. International Copyright Secured. Used By Permission.

I WONDER AS I WANDER

APALACHIAN CAROL

Arranged by Vineyard Music

Dm   **Bb**

I wonder as I wander, out under the sky

     Dm   **Bb**   **A**   **Dm**

How Jesus the Savior did come for to die

     Gm9   **(Am)**

For poor ordinary people like you and like I

   Dm   **C**   **Bdim**   **Bb**   **C**   **Dm**   **C** **Bb** **C**

I wonder as I wander, out under the sky

     Dm   **Bb**

When Mary birthed Jesus t'was in a cow stall

     Dm   **Bb**   **A**   **Dm**

With wise men and farmers and shepherds and all

     Gm9   **Dm**   **C**

But high from God's heaven a star's light did fall

   Dm   **C**   **Bdim**   **Bb**   **C**   **Dm**   **C** **Bb** **C**

The promise of ages, He then did recall

   Dm   **C**   **Bb**   **C**

If Jesus had wanted for any wee thing

   Dm   **C**   **Bb**   **A**   **Dm**

A star in the sky or a bird on the wing

     Gm9   **Am**

For all of God's angels in heaven to sing

   Dm   **C**   **Bdim**   **Bb**   **C**   **Dm**   **C** **Bb** **C**

He surely could have it, for He was the King

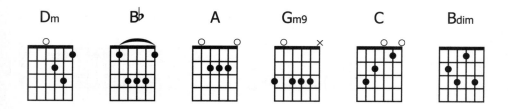

Dm   Bb   A   Gm9   C   Bdim

CCLI#3679980

Public Domain

Arr. ©2002 Vineyard Songs (SA). Admin. by Mercy/Vineyard Publishing (ASCAP) in North America.

JOY TO THE WORLD

ISAAC WATTS & GEORGE F. HANDEL
Arranged by Vineyard Music

```
      C  F            C/G  G            C
      O Amen Haleluya     O Amen Haleluya
      C  F            C/G  G         G/D C
      O Amen Haleluya     O Amen Haleluya
```

```
 C              F   C/G G   C
Joy to the world the Lord is come
C/E  F      G         C
Let earth receive her King
    C  F  C G     C   F     C
Let every heart prepare Him room
     C
And heaven and nature sing
   G                  G#dim7
And heaven and nature sing
     Am      F   C/E    F  C/G G   C
And heaven, and heaven and na-ture sing
```

```
 C              C/G G   C
Joy to the earth the Savior reigns
C/E  F       G        C
Let men their songs employ
F/G     C    F/C C        C    F/G C
  While fields and floods, rocks hills and plains
     C
Repeat the sounding joy
   G                  G#dim7
Repeat the sounding joy
    Am    C/E    C/G G   C
Repeat, repeat the  sounding joy
```

JOY TO THE WORLD - continued

ISAAC WATTS & GEORGE F. HANDEL
Arranged by Vineyard Music

D   E_m/G A_{sus} A D
He rules the world with truth and grace

D/F# G   A   D
And makes the nations prove

   D
The glories of His righteousness

 A D
And wonders of His love

  A   A#dim7
And wonders of His love

  B_m   G D/F# G A_{sus} A D
And wonders, and wonders of His love

D   G A D
Joy to the world the Lord is come

  G   A   D
Let earth receive her King

  D
Let every heart prepare Him room

  D
And heaven and nature sing

  A   A#dim7
And heaven and nature sing

  B_m   G D/F# G D/A A D
And heaven, and heaven and na-ture sing

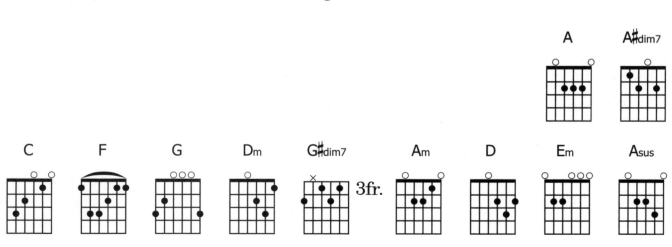

LORD COME THIS CHRISTMAS

ANDY PARK

```
    A2              Bm7/A
Away in a manger, as a child He lay
Bm7                     D/E      E       Asus   A  D/A  E/A
  Shepherds came to worship  and adore Him
    A2              Bm7/A
Deep in the meadow the angels sang
  Bm7                 Asus/E  E      Bm/A  A2      D/A  E/A
"Glory to God in the highest and peace to men"


        A    A/C#      E/D  D
    He came at Christmas
B/D#              E
     To bring His light
  E/D    A/C#            E/D  D
   To a poor and lowly manger
    A/E          Esus  E    E  Am7/C#  Bm7/D  E  C#m7  D  Esus  E
   He came that night


E          A              Bm7/A
  As You came to the manger, You have come to me
Bm7                  A/E        E      Bm/A  A  A  E/A
  You have shown the brightness  of Your glo - ry
      A            Bm7/A
And now as I worship, I have just one plea
Bm7               D/E              D/A       A  D/A  E/A  E  A/E  B/E
  As You came that Christmas, Lord please come to me
```

LORD COME THIS CHRISTMAS - continued

ANDY PARK

A/C#   E/D   D B/D#   E

Lord come this Christmas,   come bring Your light

     C#m7   E/D   D   A/E   E   Am7/C# Bm7/D# E E/D

Won't You come this Christmas, to my home, to my heart

Esus/C#   E/D   D   A/E   E   Dm9#11 Am7/C#

Lord come this Christmas to my home and to my heart

     CM9   Esus E   A2

Please come into   my heart

Esus

Dm9#11

CM9

A2

Bm7

D

E

Asus

A

B

Am7

C#m7
 4fr.

MY SOUL (MAGNIFICAT)

ADELE KANE, DAVE KANE & NICK MANDERS

E   C#m
My soul glorifies the Lord
   Bsus   E
Rejoices in God, He is holy [Repeat]

    E
He has lifted up the humble
    A
Filled the hungry with good things
 C#m7   B
His mercy frees my soul, frees me

    E
You bring joy I've only dreamed of
    A
Set my heart on fire with Your love
 C#m7   B
Your presence takes my breath away

   E   C#m7
Holy, holy is His name
      B
Holy is the Lord
     E
He is holy [Repeat]

 C#m7/A   B
My soul glorifies the Lord
 C#m7/A   B
Rejoices in You my Savior

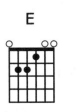

E   C#m   Bsus   A   C#m7   B   C#m7/A

CCLI#3680120

©1998 Vineyard Music (Aotearoa). Admin. by Mercy/Vineyard Publishing (ASCAP) in North America.
All Rights Reserved. International Copyright Secured. Used By Permission.

ONCE IN ROYAL DAVID'S CITY (MEDLEY)*

CECIL FRANCES ALEXANDER & HENRY J. GAUNTLETT
Arranged by Vineyard Music

F
Once in royal David's city stood a lowly cattle shed
F
Where a mother laid her baby in a manger for His bed
Bb   F/A   Gm   F   Bb   F/A   C   F Bb
Mary was that mother mild, Jesus Christ her little Child

F   C   F   Bb/D   F/C   F
He came down to earth from heaven, who is God and Lord of all
F   C   F/A   Bb   C   F
And His shelter was a stable, and His cradle was a stall
Bb   F/A   Gm   F   Bb   F/A   C   F Bb F Bb
With the poor and mean and lowly lived on earth our Savior holy

F   C   F   Bb/D   F/C   F
And our eyes at last shall see Him through His own redeeming love
F   C   F/A   Bb   C   F
For that Child so dear and gentle is our Lord in heaven above
Bb   F/A   Gm   F Bb   F/A   C   F Bb F Bb
And He leads His children on to the place where He is gone

F   C   F   Bb/D   F/C   F
Not in that poor lowly stable with the oxen standing by
F   C   F/A   Bb   C   F
We shall see Him but in heaven set at God's right hand on high
Bb   F/A   Gm   F   Bb   F/A   F/C   F
When like stars His children crowned all in white shall wait around
Bb   F/A   Gm   F   Bb   F/A   C   F   Bb
When like stars His children crowned all in white shall wait around

F   Gm   Dm/C   Bb   F/A Gm
And You, You are, You are God, You are God, God, God [Vamp]

F   Bb   F/A   Gm   C   Dm

3fr.

SHOUT [Without Capo]

SAROOP OOMMEN

Introduction: G D$_{m7}$ G D$_{m7}$ G D$_{m7}$ B$^\flat$(add9) A$_{m7}$/F

G$_2$ C/G   F   Em   D/F♯ G
Lord, You are the Son born as a child to bring new life
       C/G   F
And peace forever
          Em   D/F♯ G D$_{m7}$ G D$_{m7}$ G D$_{m7}$ B$^\flat$(add9) A$_{m7}$
A sign that will turn the world around

G$_2$ C/G   F   Em   D/F♯   G
Lord, You are the hope, nations will walk into the light
       C/G   F   Em   D   Em$_7$
Sing praise, give glory, the giver of life has made a way

     D/F♯   G   Bm F$_9$/A A G C/E F
And now, remember the days when our souls felt
F   C/E F C-B-E-F   C/E F C-B-E-F
  The power of His grace   a new covenant
F   C/E F   C-B-E-F   D$_{sus}$ D/A
  His government,   peace without end

       A G   Bm   A/D D E$_{sus}$ E
We will shout with cries of joy, the Lord our God is with us
A G   Bm   A/D D   E$_{sus}$ E
Shout! Sing and dance! (Emmanuel)We have a reason to celebrate [repeat]

Interlude: A G D$_{sus}$ D [4x]
      C$_2$ G D$_{m7}$ G D$_{m7}$ G D$_{m7}$ B$^\flat$(add9) A$_{m7}$/F

G   D/F♯   G   G/B F/C A$_{m7}$ G   D$_{sus}$/F♯ D
And right now remember the day when a manger held the King of Kings
 G
Hindi: Maseeha Ayorai (Messiah has come!) ad lib . . .

CCLI#3680168
©2002 Vineyard India Publishing. Admin. by Mercy/Vineyard Publishing (ASCAP) in North America.
All Rights Reserved. International Copyright Secured. Used By Permission.

SHOUT *[Without Capo - continued]*
SAROOP OOMMEN

Chords Used In This Song:

G   Dm7   Bb(add9)   Am7/F   G2   C/G   F

Em   D/F#   Em7   C/E   Dsus   D/A   A

Bm   A/D   Esus   G/B   F/C   Am7   Dsus/F#

SHOUT [With Capo]

SAROOP OOMMEN

Introduction: D Am7 D Am7 D Am7 F(add9) Em7/C

D2   G/D   C   Bm   A/C♯   D
Lord, You are the Son born as a child to bring new life
      G/D   C
And peace forever
               Bm   A/C♯ D Am7 D Am7 D Am7 F(add9) Em7/C
A sign that will turn the world around

D2   G/D   C   Bm   A/C♯   D
Lord, You are the hope, nations will walk into the light
      G/D   C   Bm   A Bm7
Sing praise, give glory, the giver of life has made a way

     A/C♯   D   F♯m C9/E E D G/B C
And now, remember the days when our souls felt
C   G/B C G-F♯-B-C   G/B C G-F♯-B-C
 The power of His grace   a new covenant
C   G/B   C G-F♯-B-C   Asus A/E
 His government,   peace without end

        E D   F♯m   E/A A Bsus B
  We will shout with cries of joy, the Lord our God is with us
  E D   F♯m   E/A A Bsus   B
  Shout! Sing and dance! (Emmanuel)We have a reason to celebrate [repeat]

    Interlude: E D Asus A [4x]
        G2 D Am7 D Am7 D Am7 F(add9) Em7/C

D   A/C♯   D   D/F♯ C/G Em7   D   Asus/C♯ A
And right now remember the day when a manger held the King of Kings
 D
Hindi: Maseeha Ayorai (Messiah has come!) ad lib . . .

CCLI#3680168
©2002 Vineyard India Publishing. Admin. by Mercy/Vineyard Publishing (ASCAP) in North America.
All Rights Reserved. International Copyright Secured. Used By Permission.

SHOUT *[With Capo - continued]*
SAROOP OOMMEN

Chords Used In This Song:

Capo 5

WEXFORD CAROL

PUBLIC DOMAIN
Arranged by Vineyard Music

E2   A2 A2/F#   Bm7
Good people all this Christmas time consider well and bear in mind
E2   G#m7 A2   C D E E2 A2 Bm7 G
What our good God for us has done in sending His beloved Son

E2   A2 A2/F#   Bm7
Near Bethlehem did shepherds keep their flocks of lambs and feeding sheep
E2   G#m7 A2   C D E
To whom God's angels did appear which put the shepherds in great fear

   Bm7   G2   Em7 G/D A/C# Bm7 B
"Prepare and go," the angels said, "to Bethlehem, be not afraid.
   E2 A2/F# E/G# G#m   A2   C D E E2
For there you'll find this happy morn a blessed babe, Messiah born."

Modulation: A2 Bm7 C2 G Gsus G C B♭M11 F2 G

G   C2   G2   Dm
With thankful heart and joyful mind the shepherds went the babe to find
G2   G2/B C2   E♭ F2 G
And as God's angels had foretold they did our Savior Christ behold

 Dm7   B♭ D Gm Dm/F Adim7/E Dm Dsus D
Now let our songs and praises be unto His heav'nly   majesty
 G   Bm7 G2/B C2   E♭ F2 G
And evermore amongst our mirth remember Christ our Savior's birth

G   C2 G Dm7
Good people all this Christmas time consider well and bear in mind
G   Bm7 G2/B C2   E♭ F2 G2
What our good God for us has done in sending His beloved Son

Outro: C2 Dm7 B♭M7 G2 C2 E♭ F2 G

See keyboard score for full song arrangement.

CCLI#3680199
PUBLIC DOMAIN
Arr. ©2002 Mercy/Vineyard Publishing (ASCAP).

Adoramus Te - Guitar Tablature (page 1)

Adoramus Te - Guitar Tablature (page 2)

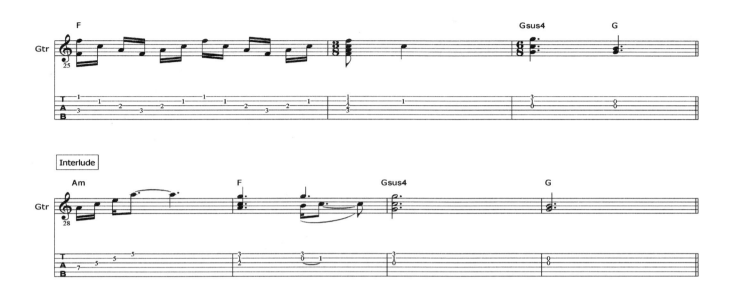

Advent Carol (Instrumental) - Guitar Tablature

Angels From The Realms Of Glory - Guitar Tablature (page 1)

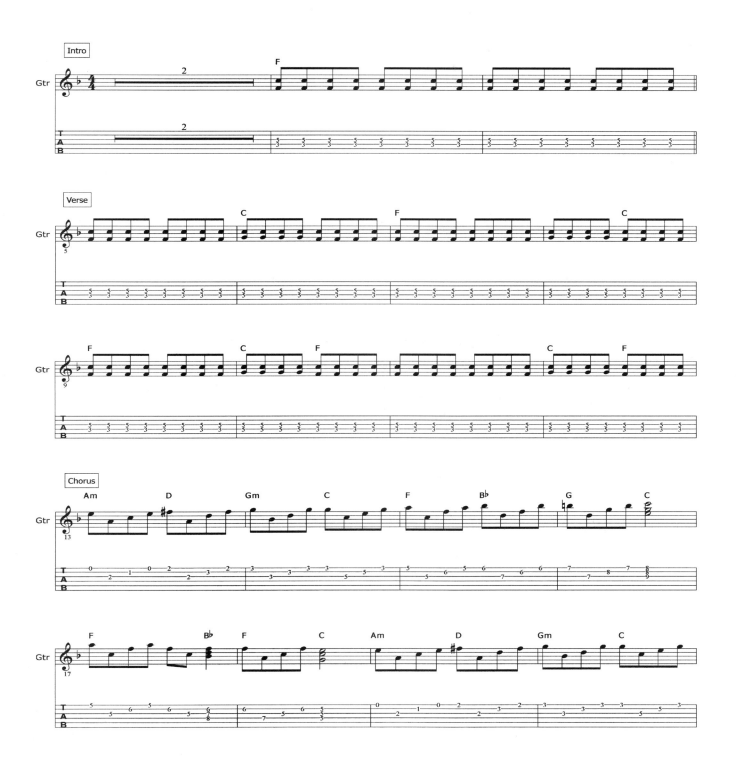

Breath Of Heaven - Guitar Tablature (page 1)

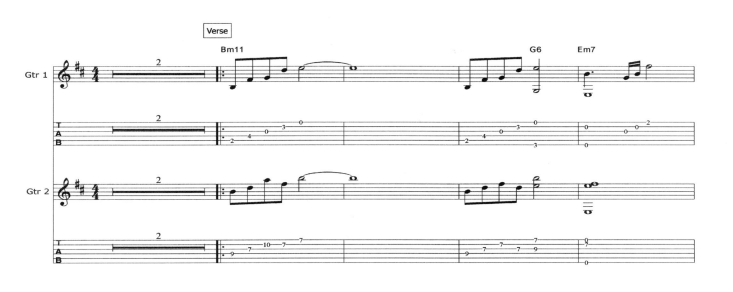

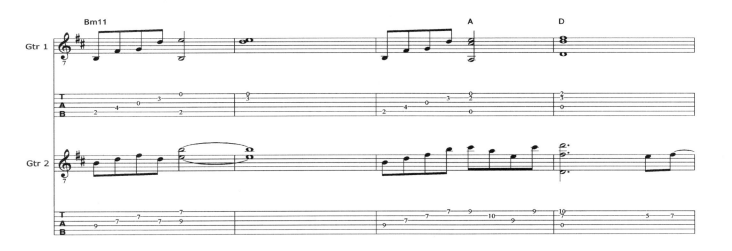

CCLI#1128784

©1992 SGO Music Publishing, Ltd. (Admin. by BUG)/Age To Age Music (Admin. by The Loving Company)
All Rights Reserved. International Copyright Secured. Used By Permission.

Breath Of Heaven - Guitar Tablature (page 3)

Breath Of Heaven - Guitar Tablature (page 5)

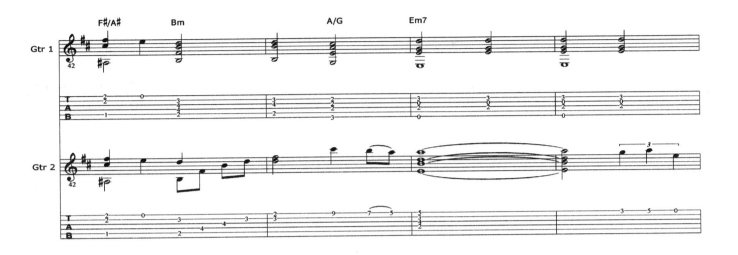

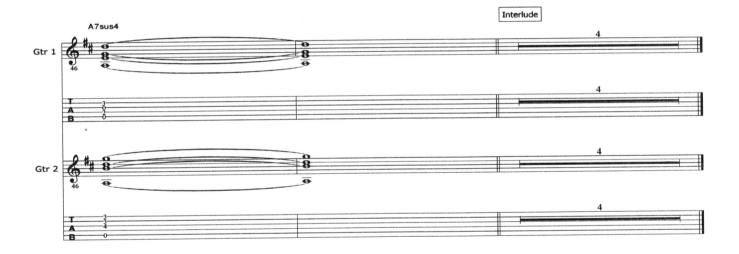

Glory To God - Guitar Tablature (page 1)

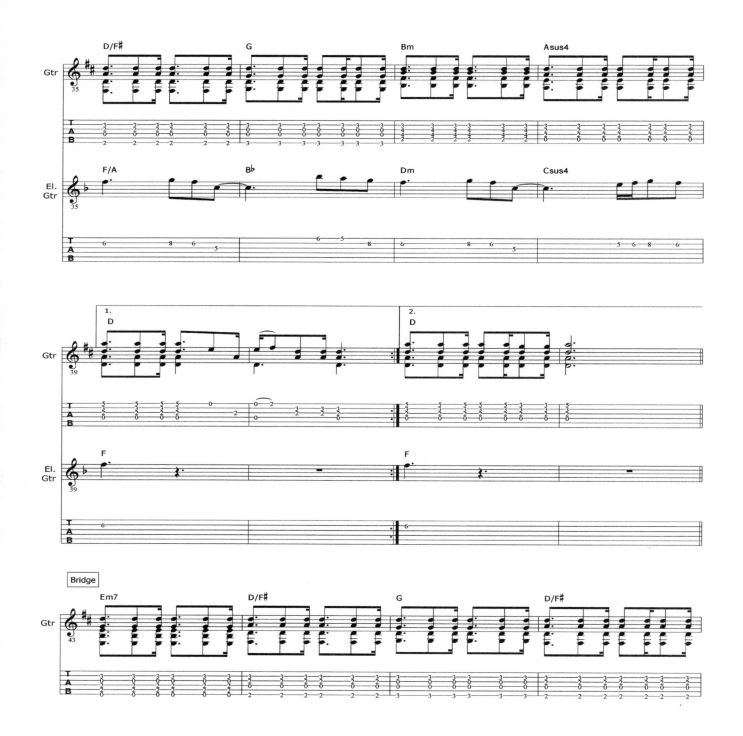

Glory To God - Guitar Tablature (page 4)

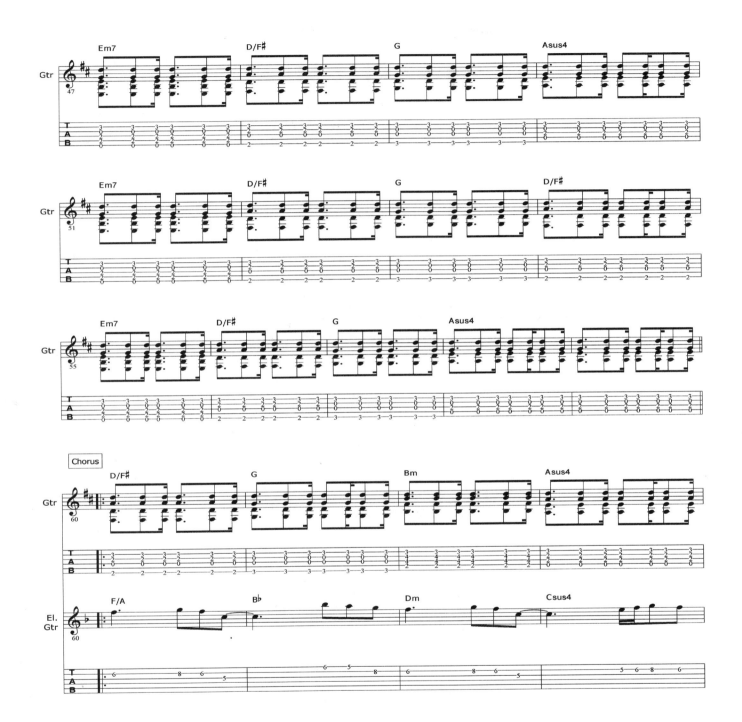

CCLI#3680326

©2002 Vineyard Songs (UK/Eire)/Mercy/Vineyard Publishing (ASCAP).
Admin. by Mercy/Vineyard Publishing in North America.

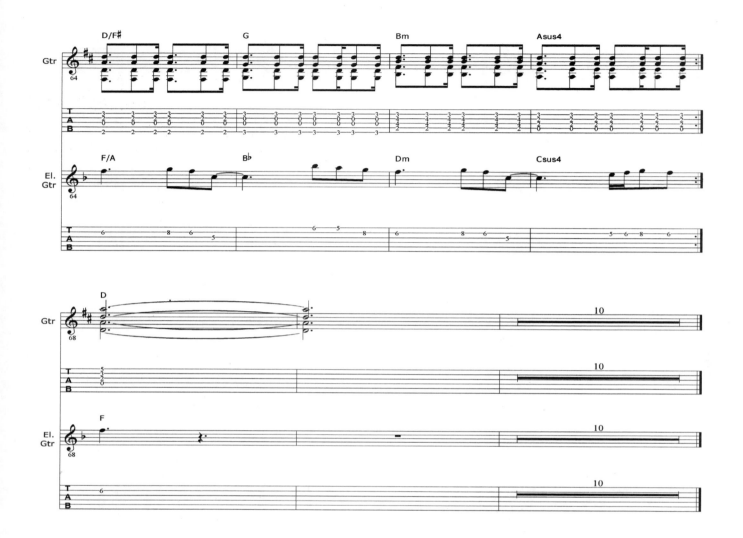

Humble King - Guitar Tablature (page 1)

Humble King - Guitar Tablature (page 2)

144

Joy To The World - Guitar Tablature (page 1)

CCLI#3679966

Public Domain

Arr. ©2002 Vineyard Songs (SA). Admin. by Mercy/Vineyard Publishing (ASCAP) in North America.

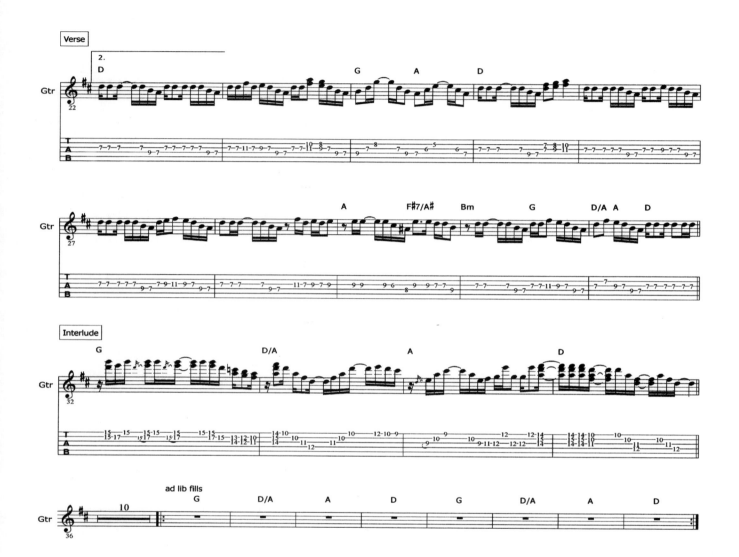

CCLI#3679966

Public Domain

Arr. ©2002 Vineyard Songs (SA). Admin. by Mercy/Vineyard Publishing (ASCAP) in North America.

My Soul (Magnificat) - Guitar Tablature

Once In Royal David's City* - Guitar Tablature (page 1)

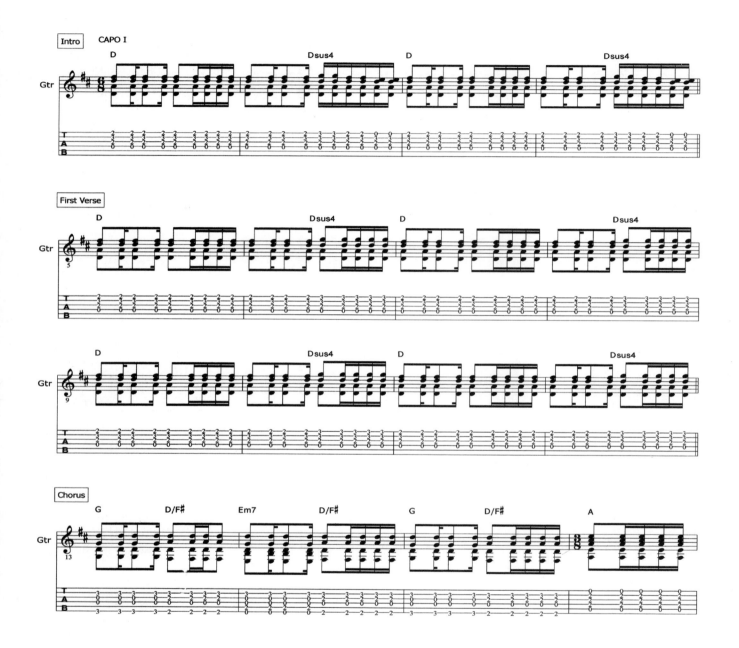

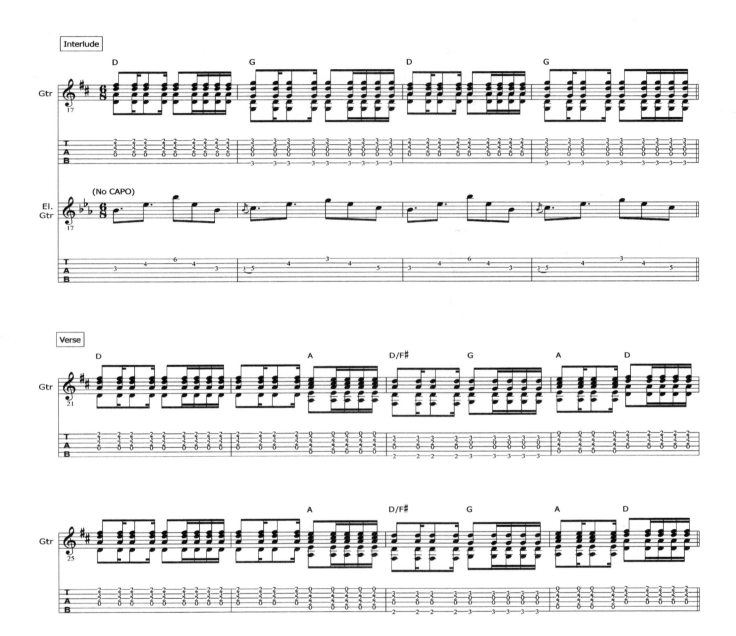

Once In Royal David's City* - Guitar Tablature (page 3)

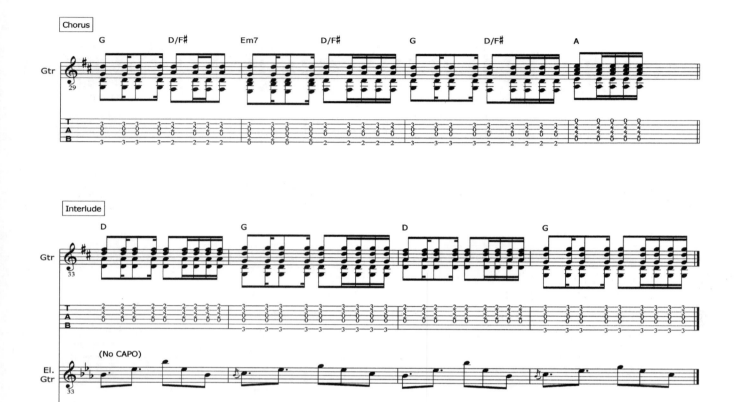

Shout- Guitar Tablature (page 1)

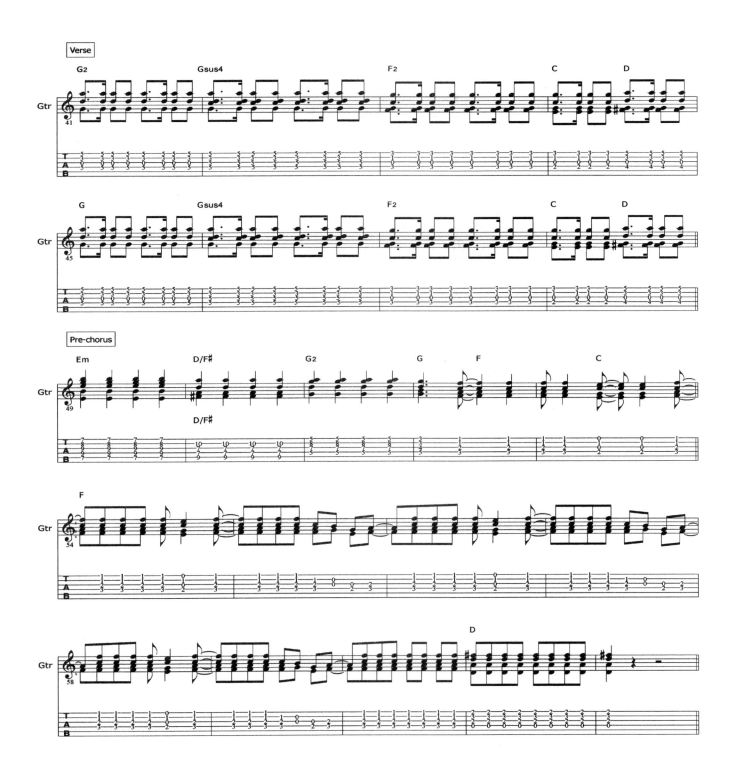

Shout- Guitar Tablature (page 4)

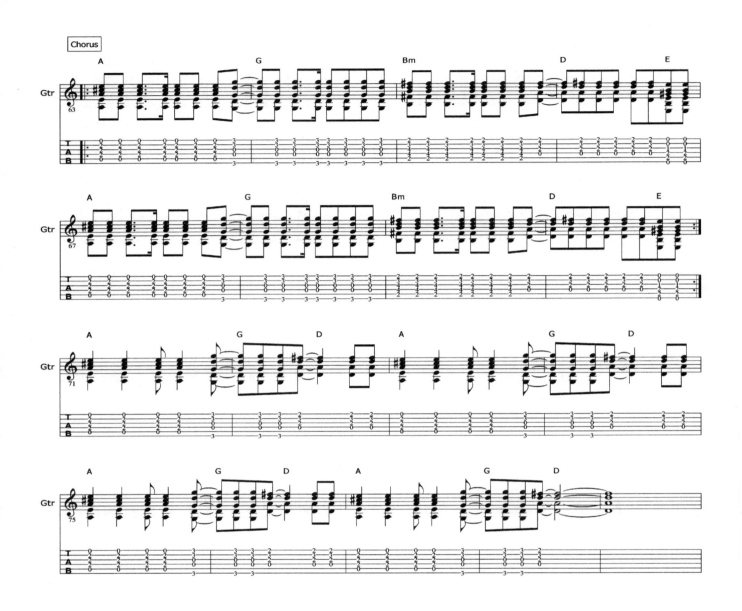

Shout - Guitar Tablature (page 5)